Mine

by

Joanna Kenrick

Illustrated by Julia Page

First published in 2009 in Great Britain by
Barrington Stoke Ltd
18 Walker St, Edinburgh, EH3 7LP

www.barringtonstoke.co.uk

ISBN: 978-1-84299-637-9

Printed in Great Britain by Bell & Bain Ltd

A Note from the Author

If you hurt someone by mistake, does that make you a bad person? What if you think you're making them happy, but then it all goes wrong?

They say love is blind. So you don't see how awful your mistakes can be.

Contents

Chapter 1

Shelly

I always knew Shelly was the girl for me. Ever since we met, way back in Year 8. She was in my form group, and I couldn't stop looking at her. She had this hair that sort of swung around, and the sweetest little giggle.

Why didn't I ask her out? Well, I was kind of shy back then. And I had bad spots for a while, and that made it worse. I thought she'd laugh at me. So I sat and looked at her from a distance. And sometimes she grinned at me, and then I felt like I was walking on air. She must have felt it too, because when she smiled at me, it was special. The smile for me wasn't like the smile she gave everyone else. I was sure of it.

I knew that one day we'd be together – I just knew it. But then Shelly started to go out with my best mate Pete.

Pete knew I liked Shelly. Or at least, he knew I liked her the year before. But I guess he forgot, or maybe he thought I didn't like her any more. Anyway – he asked her out and I was just gutted. I felt like there was something burning and bubbling inside me. Every time I saw them, it got worse.

Pete didn't understand. "You should come out with us sometime," he said. "Get yourself a date. You never have a girlfriend. What's wrong with you – you gay or something?"

So I asked Karen out. I didn't fancy her, but she said yes, so we went out with Pete and Shelly. It was a nightmare. Karen wanted to hold my hand all the time and then she got angry when I didn't want to kiss her. "Why do you keep looking at Shelly?" she snapped.

"I'm not."

"Yes you are. All the time. If you like her so much, why did you ask me out?"

I couldn't explain. "It was a mistake," I said. "Sorry."

Karen went home in a strop. Pete started getting off with Shelly. I didn't want to watch, so I went home too.

After that, I knew I had to do something.

Chapter 2

She's Mine

I waited for Shelly one day after school.

I had to make sure Pete wasn't around.

When I saw her, I grabbed her arm.

"Oh, hey, Matt," she said. "You OK?"

"You've got to stop seeing him," I said, just like that. I didn't mean to say it right out. But when I looked at Shelly, I got all mixed up in the head.

"Huh?" she said.

Then I lost all reason. I don't know what happened. It was like my mouth started talking by itself. "You should be with me," I told her. "With me. Not with him, with me. You know that, right?"

She gave me this funny look, like she wasn't sure if it was a joke. "Uh, Matt, are you OK?"

I took hold of both her arms so she was looking right at me. Being that close to her made my heart race. "Don't you see? Don't you get it? We should be together. I've known it for years."

"So why didn't you ask me out?" she said.

"I was shy," I said.

She laughed. "You don't look very shy now."

"I can't help it," I said. "I want you."

She frowned. "But I'm going out with Pete."

"I know. That's what I'm saying. You have to stop going out with him. Go out with me. Please."

She bit her lip. "Matt, I do like you, but ..."

All of a sudden I pulled her into my arms. "Listen," I said in a low voice. "Can't you feel my heart?"

She struggled a bit. "Get off, Matt." But I kept holding her. It was AMAZING to be able to smell her up close.

"Listen," I said. "Feel. Can't you tell how I feel about you?"

She pulled away. "Matt, get off. You can't just grab me like that. You don't own me. I'm not yours."

I didn't know what to say. Because I knew she was wrong. She was mine – all mine. We were meant to be together. She just didn't know it yet.

****

Pete was upset. "She broke up with me. I can't believe it!"

Nor could I. Shelly broke up with Pete! It must mean she'd come to her senses at last. She must have seen we were meant to be together.

I wasn't a very good friend to Pete. I tried to be nice about the break-up but inside I was buzzing. How long would it be before Shelly came to find me?

But she didn't. I waited – I hung around near her at school, but she never came up to me.

"Why are you hanging around all the time?" asked Kim, one of Shelly's friends.

"I'm not," I said.

"You are. It's creepy. Go away."

I looked over at Shelly. She was giggling with her friends. Just seeing that smile and hearing that wonderful giggle ... it made me feel brave. "Will Shelly go out with me?" I said.

Kim screwed up her nose. "With you?" Then she burst out laughing and walked away.

I felt hot and stupid.

Then someone told me about Rob's party.

Chapter 3

The Party

This was my big chance! Shelly was bound to be there. Pete didn't want to go because of Shelly, so I could get her all to myself!

I spent hours getting ready. I even put on some aftershave. It made my face sting but I smelled amazing. By the time I was finished, I looked really fit! How could Shelly resist me?

Mind you, I have to say Shelly looked pretty fit too. She was wearing this little purple skirt and this little pink top ... I mean, wicked!

It was like my body was on fire. My arms and legs were burning, and every time Shelly laughed, I felt a hot rush, as if I'd come too near a flame.

Then she looked up and saw me – and she SMILED. She really smiled at me! "Hi, Matt," she said. She held up a plastic cup. "Get me another vodka, will you?"

When I got back with the drinks, she said to everyone, "This is Matt. He wants to go out with me."

I took a gulp of my drink. "So?" I said.

"So what?" said Shelly.

"So will you?"

She grinned again. "You don't give up, do you?"

"No," I said. "Dance with me."

So we danced a bit and then I got her another drink. And another. The more she had to drink, the nicer she was to me. Every time her cup was empty, I put more vodka in it.

"You know what?" she said to me after a while. "You're kind of cute."

And then she leaned towards me and – well, I couldn't miss this chance, could I? So I kissed her, and then she was kissing me back and it was like – wow. I mean, really awesome. Even in my dreams it was never this good.

And then – I couldn't stop myself – I put my hands up her top. And she muttered, "Not in front of everyone." So I took her hand and led her upstairs. "Just for a minute," she kept saying.

****

I don't know whose bedroom it was. I only saw the bed – and I pushed her on to it. I could hardly breathe, I was so turned on. And she was kissing me like she was really up for it, and so I pulled her skirt up and her knickers down ...

And then ... OH my God it was so AMAZING. She was so HOT and I was burning and we were just kind of melting together.

Everything went kind of hazy, like a fuzzy mist or something. And under me, I could feel her moving. And then she was moving a

LOT, and it made me even hotter and I pushed down harder and harder.

From a long way away, I could hear Shelly saying something, but it was hard to make out the words. "Matt, stop," she said. "Stop, please ..."

I wasn't sure I'd heard her right. She wanted to stop now? But ... I was close, I knew I was!

"Stop!" Her voice shook, and she sounded out of breath.

"Just one more minute," I muttered into her hair. "One more – don't make me stop now."

"Matt, please – I don't want this!"

"Of course you do," I panted. "You know we're right together. I've known it for years."

"Please, no ..."

"Just one more second," I begged. "I'm ... oh God!"

And then ... magic! It was all just kind of WHOOOSH and I tell you it was the best feeling in the whole world. And I kind of slumped forward, and then ...

And then Shelly hit me.

Right in the face.

And the fuzzy haze was going away, and I looked down at her and she was crying.

"Why did you hit me?" I said.

"Get off, get off me!" she shouted. And she hit me again – and again.

So I got off. And Shelly jumped off the bed and pulled up her knickers and ran out of the room, sobbing.

I just lay there. What was all that about? Why did she run out on me like that? When we'd just ...

I had a big smile on my face when I went back down to the party. Those last five minutes had been the best of my life!

And then Shelly's friend Kim ran up to me and spat in my face.

Chapter 4

What's Going On?

"What's going on?" I said, puzzled.

"You bastard," she said, red from anger. "What did you do to Shelly?"

"Do to her? Nothing," I said. "What are you talking about?"

"She's crying her head off!" said Kim.

"I know," I said. "But I don't know why."

Kim made a disgusted noise. "Don't be so thick. You made her have sex with you. No wonder she's upset."

"Made her?" I said, shocked. "Of course I didn't make her. Look – she chose to come upstairs with me, didn't she? I didn't drag her up there."

"But when she told you to stop, you didn't," said Kim, her voice getting louder and louder. "You didn't listen to her. She wanted you to stop!"

"I was going to stop," I said, "but I couldn't just then ..."

"You liar!" yelled Kim. "You raped her, that's what you did! When a girl says no, she means no! You're a rapist!"

And it was like every person in that room turned to look at me.

****

I got out of there as fast as I could. Suddenly everyone was giving me angry looks and muttering about me. Someone even kicked me as I went out of the front door.

I didn't know what was going on. I felt cold. It was like I was suddenly in another world. I'd just had the best time of my life – and now this. I didn't understand. Shelly wanted to have sex with me. She kissed me – she let me pull her knickers off. OK, so maybe I didn't stop at the exact moment she

asked, but it was over soon after that

anyway. I didn't rape her. I didn't.

But I didn't sleep all night.

Chapter 5

Everyone's Wrong

Of course Pete was bound to find out. "What the hell did you do?" he yelled at me. "Everyone says you raped Shelly at Rob's party." He grabbed my shirt. "Why would you do something like that?"

"I didn't!" I said. "I would never hurt Shelly. I love her!"

Pete let go. "You love her?" he said, and he sounded disgusted. "What are you talking about?"

"I've always loved her," I said. "I loved her before you started going out with her. But then you broke up, so ..."

Pete gave me an angry look. "You are pathetic," he said. "So what happened at the party?"

I shrugged. "She went upstairs with me. We had sex. And then afterwards she said she didn't want to."

Pete frowned. "That doesn't make sense."

"I know. I didn't make her, Pete, honest I didn't."

"Well, she thinks you did."

I shook my head. "She's got it wrong. It wasn't like that."

****

Of course I tried to find Shelly at school. But every time I saw her, she ran away. And she was always with one of her friends. In class, she sat as far away from me as possible.

I couldn't understand it. I sent her notes, asking her – begging her – to go out with me. I wrote and told her how amazing she was. That I'd never met anyone like her.

Then one day Kim came up to me. "Stop writing notes to Shelly," she said. "It's freaking her out. She doesn't want anything to do with you."

"I don't understand."

"Why don't you get it?" said Kim, suddenly angry. "Can't you see what you've done to her? She's totally messed up because of you. Don't you notice anything? God, you are so selfish!" She walked away.

I was puzzled. Shelly was all right, wasn't she? What had I missed?

I started looking at Shelly more closely when I saw her in class.

OK, so her hair didn't swing like it used to. Her face looked more pale than before. Was she getting thinner? Her eyes looked at the floor most of the time. She looked nervous in class. And she didn't giggle any more.

So something must be wrong. But it wasn't anything to do with me, was it?

Chapter 6

Too Late For Sorry

Then one day I saw Shelly on her own.
She was sitting on the ground in a far corner
of the tennis court. Her friends were
nowhere to be seen.

So I went over. "Shelly?" I said.

She drew back at the sound of my voice. "Go away," she muttered.

But I sat down on the ground. "Shelly, we have to talk. I'm worried about you. You look sad. I don't understand what's going on."

"You were there," she said. "You know what happened."

"No, I don't. I thought you liked me. You came upstairs with me. You didn't stop me at the beginning."

Her fingers picked at her skirt. "I was drunk, Matt."

"So was I. So what?"

"So when I found out what was happening, I didn't want to do it any more. And you wouldn't stop." Her chin wobbled and two tears slid down her cheeks. "I asked you and asked you, but you wouldn't stop."

"But it was only another minute or so," I said. "What difference does that make?"

"It wasn't just a minute," she said. "It was ages. It felt like forever." More tears were falling onto her hands. "You made me feel dirty. You didn't listen to me. You hurt me."

"I didn't mean to," I gulped, and I reached out a hand to touch her hair. "I love you."

She jumped up as if she'd been burned. "Get off me! Get away from me!" Her hair was swinging wildly and there was terror in her eyes. "Don't you see what you've done? I can't sleep at night because I keep thinking about it! Everywhere I go, I get scared if I have to talk to a boy! It feels like everyone wants to touch me." Her hands were picking at her face, her hair, her clothes. She looked mad – like, really insane. "It feels like there's something dirty on me and I can't get it off," she muttered. "That's what you've done."

And then she turned and ran away.

And all that time she hadn't looked at me once.

****

I sat there for ages. I missed two lessons that afternoon because I was sitting there thinking.

I thought back to the party. I re-played the whole thing in my head. And I could hear Shelly's voice saying, "Stop, Matt, please."

But I didn't stop. Why didn't I? Because I was drunk? Because I was enjoying it so much?

No, I don't think it was for any of those reasons.

I think it was because I was only thinking of myself. All this time, being in love with Shelly, I only ever thought about what I wanted. I knew I loved her. I didn't ever consider if she loved me or not. I just took what I wanted.

And the worst thing is – I still love her. I always will.

But I've lost her for good. And every time I go to bed now, I won't remember the magic of that night. I'll remember her voice, begging me to stop.

I never thought I could hurt Shelley. I thought she was mine for ever. But maybe I was wrong. Maybe Shelley was never mine and never would be.

Barrington Stoke would like to thank all its readers for commenting on the manuscript before publication and in particular:

Naomi Abraham	K. Heywood
Lizzie Alder	Alwyn Martin
Amy Louise Bell	Francesca May
Iona Bolâtre-Pettit	Tim Moore
Richard Bradford	Megan O'Connor
Milo Bright	Stan Robinson
Paige Caldaralo	Michael Skeech
Lee Cornelius	Ben Thacker
Jasmine Davies	Jade Tippett
Lucy Fleming	Sophie Woodhouse
Ruth Fowler	

Become a Consultant!

Would you like to give us feedback on our titles before they are published? Contact us at the email address below – we'd love to hear from you!

info@barringtonstoke.co.uk
www.barringtonstoke.co.uk

Great reads – no problem!

Barrington Stoke books are:

Great stories – from thrillers to comedy to horror, and all by the best writers around!

No hassle – fast reads with no boring bits, and a story that doesn't let go of you till the last page.

Short – the perfect size for a fast, fun read.

We use our own font and paper to make it easier to read our books. And we ask teenagers like you, who want a no-hassle read, to check every book before it's published.

That way, we know for sure that every Barrington Stoke book is a great read for everyone.

Check out www.barringtonstoke.co.uk for more info about Barrington Stoke and our books!